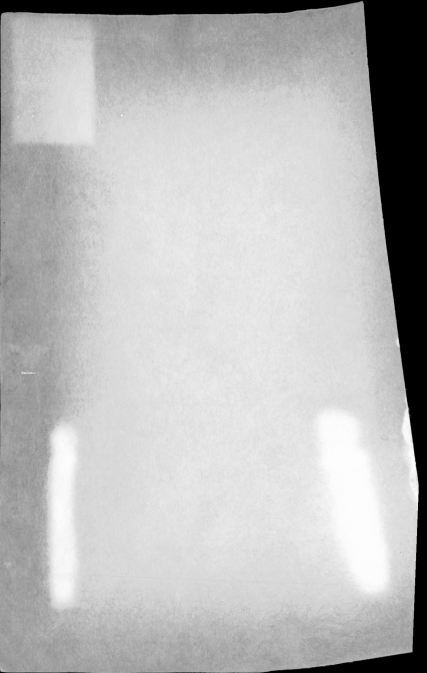

Abraham

God's Faithful Pilgrim

Ethel Barrett

Regal Books

A Division of GL Publications
Ventura, CA U.S.A.

Other good reading in this series:
Elijah and Elisha by Ethel Barrett
Joshua by Ethel Barrett
Joseph by Ethel Barrett
Daniel by Ethel Barrett
David by Ethel Barrett
Ruth by Ethel Barrett
Birth of the King by Alice Schrage
The King Who Lives Forever by Alice Schrage
Paul by Ethel Barrett
Peter by Ethel Barrett

The foreign language publishing of all Regal books is under the direction of GLINT. GLINT provides financial and technical help for the adaptation, translation and publishing of books for millions of people worldwide. For information regarding translation, contact: GLINT, P.O. Box 6688, Ventura, California 93006.

Published by Regal Books
A Division of GL Publications
Ventura, California 93006
Printed in U.S.A.

RL: 5,6
Library of Congress Cataloging in Publication Data
Barrett, Ethel.
    Abraham.

    (Great heroes of the Bible series)
    Summary: A retelling of the Old Testament story of Abraham, commanded by God to seek a new land and, later, to sacrifice his only son Isaac.
    1. Abraham (Biblical patriarch)—Juvenile literature. 2. Patriarchs (Bible)—Biography—Juvenile literature. 3. Bible. O.T.—Biography. [1. Abraham (Biblical patriarch) 2. Bible stories—O.T.] I. Title. II. Series.
BS580.A3B37 1982   222'.110924 [B]   82-12330
ISBN 0-8307-0769-7

CONTENTS

1

IN LOVE WITH A DREAM—
AND A PRINCESS

Phew!

It was the toughest exam in math so far that year. The whole class stumbled out of the school and into the streets, their eyes glazed. Abram stumbled along with them, alongside his brother Nahor. "If I live to be a thousand," Nahor said, "I'll never master math. Square root. Ugh."

"Oh yes you will, Nahor," Abram said, "and so will I. Or our father will have our hides."

Then they all began to talk at once.

"I won't master it. It's not in the stars for me."

"My stars told me not to get out of bed this morning. But my mother wouldn't listen."

They were all laughing by now, the gloom

gone. For they were out on the sunny streets, headed for home, with a few hours of freedom. And besides, the next day—no school. This seemed to dawn on everyone at once. And the whole group quickened their pace. They whistled and shouted as they scampered up the broad street, past the beautiful fountains in the courtyards of the public buildings, past the spacious library, past the temple.

There were cries of "Hurrah!" and "See ya!" as Abram and Nahor turned down the street toward their home. The two walked the rest of the way in almost complete silence, each intent on his own thoughts. And Abram's thoughts?

Muddled.

He would soon be finished with his studies and school would be behind him. His father Terah was wealthy. There was no question about Abram's future; he would follow in his father's footsteps, of course. Nothing muddling about that. The doubts in his mind were about religion.

Was it right?

And how much did he really believe in it?

And as if that were not enough to get muddled about, he had another problem.

He was in love. And though she was his half-sister, she seemed as unattainable as the stars over his head.

Her name was Sarai. And she was beautiful enough to take your breath away. People gasped at her beauty when they first saw her. Abram's stomach turned over and his knees got weak whenever he thought of her. She had him stumbling into fountains and running into brick walls.

When Abram and Nahor turned into their own courtyard, their father Terah was there, and their brother Haran. The house was built around the courtyard. It was a two-story house, large and comfortable, with plenty of room for the family, and many servants.

If all this sounds like a typical "rich kid" with problems in religion and school and love—it is. Except for one thing. Abram was real, alright, but

this story took place thousands of years ago, in the
city of Ur.

Ur was a large city, sprawled in the desert, its
temples and libraries and homes gleaming white in
the sun. It was a beautiful city, cooled by
splashing fountains in the courtyards and fanned
by palm trees clattering in the wind.

And it was a busy and prosperous city.
Treasures poured in from the Persian Gulf and
from Egypt—alabaster and copper ore and ivory
and gold and hardwoods. They came over the
great waterways, the Nile and the Tigris Rivers
and the Mediterranean Sea. And they came by
caravans through Canaan and Egypt.

It was into this culture that Abram was born.

Abram was quiet through the rest of the
afternoon and during the evening meal. In spite of
the fact that the next day was a day off from
school, a strange blanket of gloom had settled
down over his heart. That evening he sat outside
in the courtyard with his father and brothers. They

talked all around him but he did not listen. He was not thinking about Sarai now, but about the sacrifices next day. He sat there, silent, lost in his own thoughts, until darkness came.

He looked up at the moon, pale and full, and the stars. Then the chill came in over the desert air, and he shivered.

"Why so silent, my son?" It was his father Terah.

"He's thinking about Sarai," Nahor said. "He's always thinking about Sarai."

"He is almost of marriageable age," Haran said gleefully. "You can soon arrange a marriage for him. You could get him any girl he wants. But he wants Sarai."

Ordinarily Abram would blush at this, but he was only half listening. "How many years ago did our ancestor Noah live, Father?" he asked suddenly.

"Noah?" Terah said it as if he had long forgotten the name.

"Yes," Abram said, coming alive. "Noah was

my great-great-great-great-grandfather?"

"Oh, no" Terah chuckled. "He is more than that. He is about ten generations back, at least. But you are right. We are direct descendants of Noah."

"But tomorrow," Abram went on, "we will pay homage to Nana, the moon god."

There was silence, as if everyone wanted to drop the subject. But Abram persisted.

"Father, Noah worshiped only one God. The God of creation—the God of all the earth. *One* God. And now we worship Nana. And other gods too."

Terah cleared his throat. "Well, we worship one god for crops, and another god for cattle, and another god for our household—"

"But they are *idols*," Abram said.

"Well, we study the stars too," Terah replied. "Things have changed since Noah. Our thoughts have broadened. We must go along with the times."

"But, Father," Abram said, "the gods we

worship are made of wood. And silver and gold. Why, some of them are just *blocks* of wood—and the god is supposed to be somewhere *inside* those blocks. We can't even see them. Do they have ears that they can hear us? Or tongues to speak to us? What ever happened to the one God of Noah?"

"But I told you, times have changed," Terah said, uneasy now. "It's been hundreds of years since Noah worshiped the one God."

"Well, what happened to Him? Is He not still with us?"

Terah sighed. "The teachings of Noah's God have been lost down through the years. Nobody speaks of Him any more." He stirred restlessly and got up. "It's getting cold," he said. "It's time we went inside."

Nahor and Haran jumped to their feet, and the three of them started for the house, glad to have the conversation ended.

"Coming, Abram?" Terah called back.

"I'll be in in a minute, Father."

"He's usually thinking of Sarai when he's quiet," Nahor and Haran explained to their father as their voices drifted off.

Abram was alone. He got up and looked up at the sky. The stars were out plainly now—millions of them. The moon was peeking through wisps of clouds. *Did these stars have minds that they could speak? Or the moon? No.* Abram thought—*somebody created them, and that somebody did have a mind*.

There was something he should *know*, he thought, but it was beyond his grasp.

He thought of the next day. They would feast all day and dance in the market square, and then there would be the sacrifices.

Abram shuddered.

For the sacrifices would be living children—babies and toddlers. They would be hurled alive down huge ramps made of brick—and tumble into a roaring fire. He could hear in his mind the loud chanting to drown out their terrified screams.

Something was terribly, terribly *wrong*. Abram

shivered again. He pulled his robes around him and hurried toward the house.

There was Someone he wanted to worship—Someone he wanted to love with all his heart. Even more than Sarai.

Yes, even more than Sarai.

But he did not know who it was.

TWO DREAMS COME TRUE!
Genesis 11:27-30

Abram stood alone in the courtyard of his father's house. The evening meal was finished, and the night was dark and chilly. The sky was bright and clear with such a multitude of stars they seemed to touch each other in one giant blur.

It was the same courtyard Abram had stood in as a child, but nothing was the same. He was no longer the slender youth. Abram was well past his youth now—tall and muscular, with a short, curly beard and a luxurious growth of hair and bushy eyebrows. Underneath those brows his eyes were piercing, and as blue as the sky.

How the years had flown! And what a lot had happened!

Abram and his brothers were grown and

married, and his brothers had grown children by now. However, Haran had died young and left his son Lot.

Abram's mother had died too. But the wives took over running the household. There was plenty of room for all of them in Terah's big house.

In spite of the death of Haran and Abram's mother, the years had gone by happily enough. Abram watched over Lot as if he were his own son, for Abram had no children of his own.

He listened to the happy chatter back in the house and sighed with content. How he loved them all—especially his own wife. Yes—he had married Sarai, his beautiful princess. He grinned as he heard her laughter from inside the house. He was as much in love with her as he had been back in the days of his youth. *And she is as beautiful*, he thought, *as she was the day I married her*. How good life was! How good—

"Abram."[1]

A voice spoke his name. He turned to see who

it was. There was no one there. He was alone in the courtyard.

"Abram—"

There was the voice again.

Could it be—? He stood still, wondering.

"Abram," the voice went on, "get out of your country and leave your family and go to the land that I will direct you to."

This time it was plain in his heart. The voice was from God! The God Noah had known!

"Abram?"

He whirled around. This time it was his father, standing behind him. "My father!" Abram said, but he said it as if he had just been wakened from a dream.

"Are you alright?" Terah asked. "You look as if you had seen a ghost."

"Have you been speaking to me, Father?" Abram asked.

"I just said, 'Abram,' that's all."

"Is that all you said? Just Abram?"

"Of course that's all I said. What's the matter

with you?" Terah would have laughed but there was something in Abram's manner that stopped him. He backed up toward a bench and slumped down on it. Abram sat down beside him. They sat there in silence for a minute. Then, "It was God speaking to me," Abram said at last. "He told me to leave here. And go to a land where He will guide me."

"What land? Where?"

"I don't know, Father. But I am as sure as I am sure I'm sitting here that He will show me where to go."

How long they sat there after that neither of them knew. But God seemed to be right there in the courtyard, all around them.

"I'm going, Father," Abram said at last.

Terah reached over for Abram's hand and enclosed it in his own. "Then, my son," he said, "we will go."

"You, Father? It may be a long journey. And a rough one. And you are old."

"I am old," Terah said, "but I am not finished

yet. We will go. You and I and whoever wants to come with us."

"Sarai must come," Abram said. "God would not ask me to go without Sarai."

"What about Lot?" Terah asked. "You have watched over him like a father since Haran died."

"Of course, Lot. He will want to come."

Then it was as if a flood dam burst. They talked eagerly, interrupting each other as the ideas came fast, tumbling over each other.

They would go north, up along the Euphrates River. That was the main trade route. They'd go toward Haran. (Abram's brother was probably named for this city.) That would be the logical place to stop and catch their breath. Haran was 600 miles away! But so eager were they that 600 miles seemed to them like one.

And as they talked, Terah seemed to grow young again. It was nearly morning before they went back into the house and crawled into bed, too excited to sleep.

Sarai was awake. "Abram, you have been up

all night," she said. "What were you and Father talking about?"

Abram poured out the whole story to her. She listened, wide-eyed.

"But we will live like nomads!" she said. "We'll live in tents!"

"But we are rich," he cried. "We will have many tents." He spoke so loudly that she had to hush him.

"We will have many tents," he said in a whisper. "Tents for the servants, tents for the rest of the families—and a huge tent for us—as many as you wish. We will bring our rugs and our silks. You will make it like a palace!"

They were quiet for a moment, and then, "We have found God," Abram said.

When the dawn came they were still talking, making their plans. A whole new life lay ahead of them now. They did not know what lay ahead.

But they had found God!

Note

1. It does not tell us this in Genesis 11, but in Acts 7 we read that God first spoke to Abram in the city of Ur.

3

DON'T STOP NOW!
Genesis 12:1-10

Haran!

Not as big or as exciting as Ur, to be sure, but it was on the main trade routes in northern Mesopotamia, so it was important and busy enough.

Abram stood in the courtyard of the house he had rented there. His face was craggy now, and sandblasted by the desert winds. For they had traveled the 600 miles up the length of Mesopotamia—he and Sarai, of course, and his father Terah and Lot and Nahor and their large families.

"Abram."

It was God's voice again. Abram's face was not only craggy from the desert sun and wind—it

was lined with grief. For his beloved father Terah
was dead. And although it had been many weeks
since Terah died, Abram still felt the loss. His
father still seemed so close that, as Abram stood
there, it seemed as if Terah himself spoke to him.
But it was not Terah. It was the voice of God.

"Abram, I'd like to pick up the conversation
where we left off before we were interrupted."

"Interrupted, Lord?"

"Yes, Abram. And it's been a long time."

"I know, Lord. But we settled down here in
Haran. My father was old and tired and we have
relatives here—and we've accumulated many
things."

"Perhaps you've accumulated too much,
Abram."

"Yes, Lord. What is it you want me to do? Get
the tents out of storage?"

"Yes, Abram. Leave Mesopotamia behind.
This time make a clean break. And go to the land I
will show you. I'll guide you there and I'll cause
you to become the father of a great nation. I'll

bless you. I'll make your name famous. And you'll be a blessing to many others; the whole world will be blessed because of you."

Abram's heart leaped. This must mean that God was going to give him children at last!

Abram poured his heart out to Sarai that night in their room.

"A great nation? If God wants to start a new nation—couldn't He just create it Himself?" Sarai asked.[1]

"He wants to start it with a man and a woman. Someone who believes in Him. Us. I know it's almost unbelievable—"

"It *is* unbelievable!" Sarai cried. "I'm past childbearing age!"

"I don't know how He's going to do it," Abram said. "But I believe Him. And so we start packing tomorrow."

They started packing the next day.

Out of storage came the tents!

He gathered his family. Who would go with him? Not Terah, for he was dead. Nahor and his family? No. They chose to stay. And what about Lot? It turned out he was eager to go.

What a caravan they made! Even without Nahor, their possessions were greater than when they'd left Ur.

Abram did not know it, but that was the last home he would ever own or rent.

Now it was back to the life of tents. With all their wealth, the tents were huge and luxurious, to be sure, but they were still quite a comedown from the large and fine houses they'd been used to.

They followed the trade routes west, leaving behind them the great country of Mesopotamia.

The weeks flew by.

And the months.

It was nearly a year before they finally reached the land of Canaan.

The first things they saw in Canaan were the tall mountains of Gerazim and Ebal standing across from each other, a valley in between. And dotting the landscape across this vast land were walled cities belonging to the Canaanites—more idol worshipers!

While his servants were busy getting tents pitched and provisions unpacked, Abram went a distance away and leaned against an oak tree. He looked up at the sky, and listened. *What a dreadful place!* he groaned in his soul.

Did I hear you right, Lord? And if I did, what are you trying to do to me? And as he stood there and looked across the great expanse of land, a great silence settled over him and he found himself trembling. And he knew that he was again in the presence of God. And God's voice came to him, full-blown in his mind. "I know, Abram. This land is filled with Canaanites now. But it is to your descendants I'm going to give it."

And Abram believed Him. And he took some stones and built an altar to the Lord God.

He staked his claim in the land of Canaan.

The place was called Shechem.

In the months that followed, they journeyed slowly south, following the good pasturelands, down through the rolling hills, and finally into the great desert Negeb. And everywhere they stopped, Abram built altars to God. The pasture was still good, for it was during the winter months.

But then—

The summer months came. And there was no rain. And they were surrounded by miles and miles of dry, cracked earth. And there was no pasture for their flocks.

But did Abram turn to God?

No.

Sad to say, he turned to his own thinking.

He looked down toward Egypt.

Egypt! That rich and fertile country, nourished by the river Nile. There was no famine there.

It was there Abram decided to go.

That was his first mistake.

Note

1. Genesis 12:1-3. This great nation would first be called the Hebrew nation, and God's people would be called Hebrews.

4

THE LIE
Genesis 12:9-20

Egypt!

What an exciting country! More exciting than anything in Mesopotamia had ever been!

The great River Nile ran down through the center of it, with rich, fertile land on either side.

And the great pyramids! Built of thousands of blocks of granite, each one weighing several tons!

While Abram's servants went to work pitching tents and settling the families, Abram wandered through the city's broad streets and vast treasures like a bedazzled tourist. No tales he had ever heard about this land could come up to the reality of its wealth and beauty. Why the Pharaoh had collected treasures from all over the world.

He also collected beautiful women.

Beautiful women!
Sarai!

Abram's amazement and delight turned to fear. And his great faith in God began to wobble a bit.

Because of his great wealth and enormous tents that were now being pitched, he knew that he would sooner or later come to the attention of Pharaoh. He knew he would be royally received in the palace. What if—what if—

What if the Pharaoh wanted to add Sarai to his collection of beautiful women?

Abram made a U-turn with his elaborately bedecked camel and hastened back to Sarai. And as he traveled back, his faith that had already become wobbly, collapsed.

When he got back, their luxurious tent had already been bedecked with their rugs and silks, and Sarai was sitting on a pile of rugs made into a silken couch. He took a few steps toward her. And then stopped short. In spite of her years she was still a striking beauty. All the sun and wind that had crinkled Abram's face had left her untouched.

Abram opened his mouth to speak. And when the words came out he could hardly believe he was saying them. But say them he did.

"Sarai," he stumbled through the words— "You are still a beautiful woman. If you come to the Pharaoh's attention—no, *when* you come to the Pharaoh's attention—for you surely will—he may—he just may—"

"What my husband?" Sarai asked. "He just may what?"

"He just may want to add you to his collection of beautiful women, Sarai. If he thinks you are my wife—he will *kill* to get you!"

"Kill!?!" she asked. "Who? When?"

"Kill *me*," Abram blurted out. "And as soon as possible."

They stared at each other.

"Say you are my sister, Sarai," he said miserably.

"That would be a lie," she said.

"But you are my *half*-sister."

"That would be *half* a lie, my husband," she

said. "And a half a lie is as good as a whole one—or as bad. Why do you ask this of me? Why are you doing this to me?"

"Because—" and the words stumbled out, for his faith had entirely collapsed by now. "I have to do this. Say you will do it, Sarai, and you will save my life."

In the end, Sarai agreed. He could see that she was not happy about it.

What he could not see at the moment was that God was not too happy about it either.

He found out soon enough.

For because of Abram's wealth he soon came to the attention of the Pharaoh. And so did Sarai.

When the princes of the palace saw her they praised her to the Pharaoh. And when the Pharaoh saw her he agreed with them. She would make a beautiful addition to his collection.

And when he was told that Sarai was Abram's sister—he took her into his household and added her to his harem!

Abram spent many hours and sleepless nights

pacing back and forth, wringing his clammy hands, wondering what would become of Sarai.

He paced in his tent.

He paced in the palace courtyards.

His beautiful Sarai!

The Pharaoh heaped riches upon him—more cattle, more servants, more slaves, more silver and gold—and all because of his "sister"!

But he was despondent. He did not want more wealth—he wanted his wife back.

Of all creatures under the sun, he was one of the most miserable. What had he done? And now what could he *do*?

Well he could do nothing. But God was still there.

For suddenly—

Sickness fell upon Pharaoh's household!

One by one, then two by two—then by the dozens, people fell sick and were confined to their beds. First among the servants, then among the officials—then Pharaoh himself.

And then, finally, the word got out.

Sarai—whom Abram had said was his
"sister"—was really his *wife*!

Pharaoh was furious. He sent for Abram.

"What have you done to me?" he demanded.
"Why didn't you tell me she was your wife? Why
were you going to let me marry her, thinking she
was your sister?"

Abram just stood there, his hands dangling,
his tongue cleaving to the roof of his mouth. He
had no answer.

"Take her—" screamed Pharaoh "—and be
gone!"

Abram stumbled backwards to leave the room.
So befuddled was he that he bumbled into the
curtains at the door. He disentangled himself and
stumbled down the corridor.

A few moments later Sarai was delivered to
him. He was so ashamed he could scarcely look at
her. She bowed her head and followed him in
silence out of the palace.

Within a week they were packed and on their
way out of Egypt. They did not speak during the

packing. They scarcely spoke for days. Abram left with twice as much wealth as he'd had before.

And among the slaves was a beautiful young Egyptian girl, Hagar, whom Sarai wanted as her personal slave.

Abram was lower than he'd ever been before. It was one of the darkest chapters of his life.

And Hagar? She was to figure in both of their lives—more than either of them dreamed at the time.

5
THE CHOICE
Genesis 13—15

"Uncle Abram," Lot said, and his eyes were flashing, "the time has come to do something."

Ah, the explosion finally came. Abram had been looking for it.

They'd been back in Canaan for some time. The famine was over. The rains had come, and the land was fertile again. The pastures were lush and green—and there was plenty of food for their flocks.

Abram looked at Lot standing before him, his short-cropped, dark beard bristling, his short, dark, curly hair framing his head, aquiver in the breeze.

How much he looks like his father Haran, Abram thought. Haran, who had died so young, and left Abram to look after Lot since he had been a child; indeed Lot seemed to Abram like his own son.

Abram looked at him patiently now. "I know, my son. I know our herdsmen have been fighting. I know they are becoming violent. But we have expanded and grown—"

"Expanded!" Lot shot back. "We have overlapped! That's just the problem. I can't tell where my cattle end and yours begin. We've got to do something—and soon!"

Abram sighed. "Lot," he said softly, "you've had free choice. No one forced you to come along with us when we left Ur. And no one can force you to stay with us now. But there's no reason why we should have to quarrel over this."

Lot relaxed a bit.

"Look," Abram went on. "Look as far as you can see. There is the whole land before us. There is surely room for us both. Leave if you want to. And the choice is yours. If you want to go to the left, then I'll go to the right. If you want to go to the right, I'll go to the left."

Lot suddenly went limp. "You mean you are giving me a choice? That I can take any part of the land I want?"

Abram nodded.

Lot turned then and looked down at the well-watered Jordan valley—lush and green—far more valuable than the hills where they were standing. "All right, Uncle Abram," he said at last. "I'll take my family down there."

They embraced then, briefly; Abram felt Lot already tugging away in his mind, anxious to be on his own.

Within a week Lot was packed with his family and all his possessions. And as Abram watched them go, his heart was like lead, for Lot was like his own son. But at last the tail end of Lot's huge caravan disappeared—down through the hills and into the valley. And Abram stood there alone; he had never felt more alone in his life.

And then—

"Abram."

The voice of God again!

"Lift up your eyes, Abram, and look. Look north. Look south. Look east and west. For all the land you see, I'm going to give to you and your descendants forever."

Abram sank to his knees.

"Yes," the voice went on. "I'll make your descendants so many they'll be like the dust of the earth. No one will be able to count them."

Abram never knew how long he stayed there. It was late in the night when he got back to his tent.

Sarai was awake, waiting for him. "You've been gone a long time," she said. "Why did you stay out there so long? You were thinking of Lot?"

"Lot had his choice," Abram said, "and he made it. I had to let him go." And then he told Sarai what God had said to him.

"What do we do now?" she asked.

"We pack the tents," Abram said, "and move on."

"But where are we going?"

Sodom and deposited the treasures he had captured.

The king of Sodom, back from the hills, was beside himself with joy, gratitude and praise.

"The treasures you got back," he cried, "take them—take them all. The gold, the silver, everything—take it with my thanks!"

Abram stared at the king of Sodom from beneath his bushy eyebrows. "Thanks, but no thanks," he said. "All I want is expenses—for my trained men and for my friendly neighbors who left their families and risked their lives to help me."

The king was speechless with astonishment.

Lot was speechless with shame.

"But for myself," Abram said, "I want nothing. I will not have it said that the king of Sodom made me rich."

He glanced at Lot.

Lot stared at the ground.

"I'm going home," Abram said. "And you, Lot? Are you staying?"

There was an embarrassed silence. And then, "I'm staying," Lot said sheepishly.

Abram turned on his heel, and without another glance back, began to issue orders to his men to get ready to leave.

Lot stared after him. Clearly, his fuddy-duddy old Uncle Abram was a man to be reckoned with. He now had the respect not only of everyone up in the hills but all the kings of the valley.

Abram returned home triumphant, to be sure, but exhausted. And discouraged. For Lot had chosen to stay in Sodom. And he, Abram, still had no son.

Sarai fluttered over him like a mother bird. She ordered the servants to prepare him a bath, and then a feast. But nothing could raise his spirits.

And then God's voice came again.

"Abram."

Abram was out under the stars. He had wandered out there from his couch, unable to sleep. When he heard his name he sank to his knees and listened.

"Don't be afraid," God said. "I will befriend you, and give you great blessings."

- "But what good are all the blessings when I have no son?" Abram cried.

"You will have a son to inherit everything you own, Abram. Look at the stars. Count them, if you can. Your descendants will be like that—too many to count. I'll make a covenant with you right now—a contract. Believe me!"[1]

Abram slid forward from his knees and lay on the ground, his head cradled in his arms.

"I believe you, Lord," he said. And he fell into a deep sleep—the first real sleep he had known since his return from the valley.

Note

1. See Genesis 15:1-6.

6

DON'T TAMPER WITH A PROMISE
Genesis 16:1-13

The idea seemed reasonable enough to Sarai when she first thought of it. It was the duty of every wife in those days to give her husband children. If she could not give him children herself, it was her duty to see that he got them one way or another. So if she, Sarai, could not give Abram the son he wanted, it was up to her to supply him with a wife who could.

After all, it was the accepted custom of the day.

Now once the idea got into Sarai's head, it began to grow—like rolling a snowball downhill—it got bigger and bigger, until finally she could think of nothing else.

So, as the days went on she found herself

watching Hagar, the beautiful slave they had brought back from Egypt for her personal maid.

She watched Hagar as the girl moved with quiet grace about her duties. The girl was a beauty, no doubt of that. And strong and healthy to boot. She'd make a perfect mother for the son she and Abram wanted.

"But, Sarai, you are my first love," Abram protested when she told him about it.

"I know I am, Abram," she said. "But this will make no difference with us. She will bear the child for *me*. It will be like my own. And we can go on as before and be happier than ever together."

Well it seemed like a good idea at the time.

Just one little problem.

God was not in on it.

But at Sarai's insistence it was done. Hagar became, in a sense, Abram's "second wife." And everything was as Sarai had said it would be. They got along fine, like a happy family, the three of them—Abram, Sarai and Hagar. And things went swimmingly—for a few months.

But then it was confirmed—a baby was on its way.

And then—

The last thing Abram or Sarai would have dreamed possible came to pass!

The trouble started slowly.

At first Sarai thought she was imagining it.

It seemed that Hagar was a little slower in obeying Sarai's orders. She dragged her feet when she was sent to do her chores.

Then there were haughty stares. And Sarai found to her amazement that Hagar could stare her down any day.

Then the haughty stares turned to saucy remarks.

Then Sarai exploded.

"She's getting to be impossible!" she said to Abram.

"Well, perhaps she's just a little nippy," Abram said. "Be patient with her. She is very young—"

"A little nippy! A *little* nippy! She's walking around here like a queen! She treats me as if *I* were the slave! She has forgotten that *she* is the slave. *I* am the mistress in this household!"

"Of course," Abram said. "She is your slave, Sarai. Do with her as you wish. It's up to you to set her straight."

Sarai calmed down then. She had Abram's permission to straighten out Hagar. And she set about to do it.

With a vengeance.

She'd teach Hagar not to put on airs!

And Hagar?

The sudden turnabout hit her like a thunderclap.

Her tasks were increased. Her hours of work were lengthened. Abuses were heaped upon her head.

This calm and beautiful household was turned into a battleground. And this queenly Sarai, who had always been like a mother to Hagar, suddenly turned into a shrew!

Now Hagar's arrogance turned to fear. And homesickness. She was no longer wanted, no longer accepted. She was a stranger in a strange land.

At last she could bear it no longer. She decided to run away.

She watched for a chance.

And when the opportunity came she sneaked out of the compound, away from the cluster of tents, and slipped away into the wilderness.

First she ran.

Then she walked.

Then she trudged along, weary and frightened nearly out of her wits. If only she could find her way to a trade route and join a caravan and somehow get back to Egypt! But she was alone and without money and without protection. She was doomed to Sarai's abuse if she went back— and doomed to die if she went on!

She sank down to the ground, sobbing and exhausted.

And then—

"Hagar." It was a voice, unlike any voice she had ever heard before. She struggled to a sitting position. The sun was low now, almost ready to set, and its slanting rays shone in her eyes so she could scarcely see the figure standing before her. But a great calm came over her spirit. "I'm running away from my mistress Sarai." she said. "My life is miserable; I don't know what else to do."

"I'll tell you, Hagar," the voice came back. "Go back to your mistress—"

"But I don't want—"

"Whether you want to or not."

"But—"

"No buts, Hagar. You will be safe. And your baby will be safe. He will be a son. And you are to name him *Ishmael*. It means 'God hears.' He will be a wild sort of a man, Hagar. And he will not live peaceably in the heart of the family. He will depart from it—but not too far. He will always live close by."

Hagar crouched on the ground, looking up.

The sun was directly in her eyes now, blinding her. She realized suddenly that He was gone.

I have seen God, she thought. *I have seen God—and lived to tell about it*!

She cupped some of the cool spring water in her hands, and drank some and drenched her face with it. Then she got up and started back.

She dreaded the thought of facing Sarai, but her foolish plan to run away could end up with her own death. At least back with Sarai and Abram she would have protection. But most important of all, she would be obeying God. "I have seen God—and lived," she kept saying aloud as she hurried back.

7

A REAL PRINCESS AND A NEW PROMISE
Genesis 16:15—17:21

"Bad boy!"

"Have you been teasing the herdsmen again?"

"Clown!"

"Lovable."

"Yes, lovable—*sometimes*!"

"Monster!"

"What? You tease the herdsmen only in sport? Well, it wasn't sport to them, young man."

"What? Going through a phase? And which phase is this?"

"Good debater? What do you mean, good debater? Scrappy kid is what he is."

"Isheeeeee! Ishmael, come here at once!"

"He's impossible!"

Abram tossed restlessly on his couch, thinking

of all the things that had been said to and said about Ishmael that day. God had given him a son alright—but what a son!

Yes, Hagar had returned to the camp and had born Abram the child and had named him Ishmael as God had instructed. God had told Hagar that her son would grow up to be a wild sort of a man.

Abram groaned and turned over on his side. God hadn't been joking! He had meant every word of it. Ishmael was "thirteen going on thirty." And no matter how much Abram loved him, he had to admit that Ishmael was just that—a scrappy kid.

And Hagar and Sarai? Well, they had made their peace—at least they decided to put up with each other for the child's sake.

Sometimes there were long days of stony silence. Sometimes there was peace on the surface. Hagar humbly obeyed, but her eyes were flashing with anger she could not express. And sometimes there were violent quarrels. It was always Hagar who simmered down first, though, for she never forgot what God had commanded her to do—be submissive to Sarai. *And when they are at peace*, Abram thought, *they're peaceful on the outside and fighting on the inside.* He groaned again.

"Abram."

Abram snorted and sat up straight on his couch. It was God's voice. Had he been just thinking these thoughts, sort of dreaming with his eyes open? Or had he been talking aloud? "Yes, Lord," he whispered in the darkness.

"Abram, I want to renew our contract. And I'm going to change your name. It is time."

Abram glanced across the huge tent at Sarai. She was stirring in her sleep. Then he jumped from his couch and went outside the tent, under the stars. Better finish this conversation in private. "Yes, Lord," he whispered, and fell to his knees on the grass. "We can talk now."

"We can talk anywhere I please," the voice came back. "I just happened to choose now."

"You mentioned a contract, Lord?"

"Yes, Abram. A contract between us. For I

intend to make you into a nation—a mighty
nation. Multitudes."

"You keep repeating yourself, Lord."

"You'd be amazed at how much I have to keep
repeating myself, Abram. People don't listen."

Abram slid forward on his face. "I'm
listening, Lord."

"I am also going to change your name. You
will no longer be Abram. You will be called
ABRAHAM from now on." (*Abraham* means
"Father of nations.")

"*How?* Abraham thought. *Through whom? It
must be through Ishmael.* "Thank you, Lord," he
said.

"Hold it," the Lord said. "Just a minute. It
takes two to make a contract. And your part of the
contract is to obey."[1]

"Yes, Lord."

"And as for Sarai. I'm changing her name too.
Her name will be *Sarah*."

Sarah! Sarah meant princess! His boyhood
thoughts of her stirred in Abraham's memory. He

had always thought of her as a princess. And now she was a princess indeed. His beautiful princess!

"And I will give you a son by her."

Wait a minute. *Wait a minute.* Had God really said that? No, He couldn't have. He must have meant that He would start the nation with Ishmael. "Yes, God, I heard you," Abraham said. "Do bless Ishmael."

"No, you didn't hear me, Abraham. I said that *Sarah* would bear a son."

Abraham buried his face in the grass—as if he could hide it from God. For he was laughing inside. Sarah and him to have a baby? Ridiculous!

"You are to have a son," God was saying, "and you are to name him ISAAC. Isaac means laughter."

Oh, no. There was no hiding anything from God; God knew his thoughts.

"And as for Ishmael," God went on, "I'll bless Ishmael. He will multiply too, and become a great nation. My contract with you does not include Ishmael. This thing is going to come about through Isaac. It is *Isaac* who will be born to you and Sarah."

Long after God had stopped speaking, the words were ringing in Abraham's ears. *You and Sarah. A son. You and Sarah . . .*

It was a long time before Abraham went back to the tent and lay down on his couch. *God and I are talking back and forth like friends now*, he thought. With every conversation he found that more and more he could speak from his heart, pouring out his thoughts in a jumble, no matter how ridiculous they might sound. But his words were always spoken with awe and reverence, no matter how they may sound as they came tumbling out. He knew that God knew his heart.

He was still thinking about this when the first streaks of dawn came over the countryside, and the sounds and stirrings of another day began.

"Bad boy!"

"Clown!"

"Isheeeeee! Ishmael, come here at once!"

"Have you been teasing the herdsmen again?"

"He's impossible!"

"Monster!"

It was easy to see that Ishmael was up and stirring.

"Oh, Lord," Abraham groaned, "the day has scarcely begun and Ishmael is in trouble already."

And he rolled over on his side for another forty winks.

Note

1. Another part of this contract was circumcision. You can read about it in Genesis 17:9-14.

8

THREE STRANGERS AND A BARGAIN
Genesis 18

Phew!

It was *hot*.

Abraham sat outside his tent, leaning against the trunk of an oak tree. He watched a fly crawl slowly down one of the stripes in his robe. It was too hot to bother to brush it away. It finally made up its own mind to leave. He watched as it flew just a foot or two away and landed on the petals of a wind flower, sending it abobbing. He shifted his position and scratched his back on the rough bark of the oak tree.

This was a different kind of heat. It was the kind that not only dampened the body but dampened the spirits too. The kind that brought out the worst in you. The kind that could make

Sarah and Hagar burst out in a knock-down-drag-
'em-out fight.

No—it's more than just the heat, Abraham
thought, shifting uneasily. For he was used to
quarreling. And feeling depressed. These things
came and went; they were a part of life. But this
heat bore with it a sense of coming disaster—like
the eerie calm before a storm. Something terrible
was going to happen; he felt it in his bones. Some
calamity, some upheaval. It was worse than the
feeling that somebody was going to pull the rug
out from under you. It was more like the very
earth was going to be yanked out—

Ho—

What was this?

There were three men coming toward the tent
compound. They weren't his herdsmen or his
servants. He could see by their clothing that they
were strangers.

Now it was the custom in that part of the
country to be super polite to guests. It was not
enough to wait until they got to your door—you

ran out to greet them.

Abraham got to his feet, as fast as the heat and his cramped legs would allow him, and hurried toward them. "Greetings," he said when he got up to them, and he bowed. "If you are traveling, my dear sirs, do not go another step until you have stopped and refreshed yourselves. It is far too hot to go on." He could not have been more cordial if they had been from heaven itself.

He led them back to the shade of the oak tree. He clapped for servants to bring some rugs to spread on the ground. And he bade the visitors to sit there in the shade. "I'll have water fetched to wash your feet."

He left them there reclining in the shade and sprang into action, giving orders.

"Sarah! Cakes from your finest meal! Milk! Cheese!"

And to the servants, "Butcher a calf—one of the finest!"

Sarah sent servants in every direction. Abraham selected the calf himself to make sure it was just right.

Now all this was *not* done in a minute; a fine feast like this took a bit of time. But then, no one was in a hurry.

It was late afternoon when Abraham finally served his guests. He served them himself, for somehow he sensed that he was in the presence of greatness. He stood beside them in respectful silence as they ate, ready to take care of their slightest need. And then one of them said something that brought Abraham up with a jolt.

"Where is your wife Sarah?"

It came out of the blue. Who had said it? Surely not one of the strangers. This was a personal question. His bushy eyebrows went up in a question.

"Where is your wife Sarah?"

It *did* come from one of them.

"She's in the tent," he said, and his scalp prickled. Then—

"Next year at about this time, I will give you and Sarah a son."

This time Abraham felt as if he'd been struck by a bolt of lightning. He *was* in the presence of greatness. For it was the Lord! Come to earth in a man's body! And he was not the only one who heard the voice!

"Why did Sarah laugh?" the Lord said.

"Laugh?" Abraham was dumbfounded. But the Lord nodded. Then He went on, "And why did she say, 'Can a woman my age have a baby'?"

"I did not hear her laugh—" Abraham stammered.

"Is anything too hard for God?" the Lord interrupted. "Next year, just as I told you, I will certainly see to it that Sarah has a baby—a son."

"But I didn't laugh." It was Sarah, standing in the door of the tent.

Abraham turned and looked at her. "I didn't hear her laugh—" Abraham began again, and he saw Sarah's face. She was lying. And she was frightened out of her wits. She *had* laughed in her mind, and the Lord knew it.

"I didn't laugh," she said again weakly, and her voice was a high tremolo, and it wobbled off in a little trill that was almost a nervous giggle.

Abraham did not dare to say more. It was plain to everyone that she was lying.

And then to his immense relief the men stood up. The subject was closed. Sarah backed into the tent and disappeared from sight.

Moments later the travelers indicated that they had to be on their way. And Abraham indicated that he would walk part way with them.

Phew!

That was quite a visit. It left him weak and shaken. But why, he wondered, did he still have this feeling of coming disaster? It came back now, stronger than ever; he could not shake it off.

"Shall I hide my plan from Abraham?"

Abraham turned sharply to the one who had spoken. It was the voice of the Lord. But hide what? What was God about to do?

The Lord answered his unspoken question.

"I have heard that the cities of the plains are utterly evil. And the most wicked of them all are Sodom and Gomorrah."

Lot! Abraham's heart sank.

"And I have come down to see if these things are so."

By now they were at the brow of the hill, looking down over the plains. The other two men went on ahead and started down the hill. Abraham and the Lord were alone.

And Abraham's thoughts were in a turmoil. *Why would God make a trip down to the plains to see what was going on inside Sodom? Doesn't He know what is going on down there? And doesn't He know that Lot is in Sodom? Doesn't God know everything? And why does He choose to stand here and discuss it with me, Abraham?*

The answer came like a bolt. God had limited Himself to come in a man's body so Abraham could stand there, eyeball to eyeball—*and argue with Him*. He was *inviting* Abraham to bargain with Him!

It was so astonishing that Abraham nearly fell flat on his face under the weight of it all. He swallowed hard, though there was not a drop of spittle in his mouth. "And if they are as evil as you say, you are going to destroy them," he finally managed to say.

The stranger nodded.

"But won't you be killing the innocent with the wicked? Supposing there are fifty godly people inside Sodom? You would be killing them too. Couldn't you spare Sodom for their sakes? Surely you wouldn't do a thing like that. You are *God*. Shouldn't you be fair?"

And the stranger said, "Very well, then, if I find fifty godly people there I'll spare the city for their sakes."

Abraham did some quick calculations. Fifty people. Would there be that many among Lot's family and servants? No, he was afraid not. He looked at the stranger desperately.

"I know I am but dust and ashes—but please let me go on. Suppose there are only forty-five?"

And the answer came back—"I will not destroy it if I find forty-five."

I am talking to God, Abraham thought. *I must*

be out of my mind to be so bold. But he went on.
"Suppose there are only forty?" He felt as if he
had swallowed a bellyful of pinwheels and they
were all going around as he waited. But the
answer came back, "I won't destroy it if there are
only forty."

Abraham felt his scalp prickle now. "Please
don't be angry," he said, "but I have to say it;
suppose there are only thirty?"

"I won't do it if there are thirty."

Abraham said it aloud this time, "I know I am
speaking to God. I don't know how I dare—but I
can't stop now. Please let me go on; suppose there
are only twenty?"

He looked hard at the stranger. Were the
corners of His mouth twitching—just a little—in a
beginning smile? Was that compassion in His
eyes? Abraham's own eyeballs seemed to be
jumping in his head. Would there be twenty in
Lot's family? Would there be twenty? *Would there
be twenty?* He closed his eyes to stop the jumping.

"Oh, Lord, don't be angry," he said. "I'll

speak just once more—just once more. Suppose—
only ten?" And his voice was shaking now. He
was on the verge of tears. "For the sake of ten,
Lord, for the sake of ten?"

He had stood as long as he could. His knees
turned to rubber. They gave way and he sank to
the ground in the path. He knew in a minute he
would be sobbing. He felt a hand on his head.
And then, "For the sake of ten I won't destroy
it."

That touch of the hand on his head was tender.
And then the stranger was gone and Abraham was
alone in the path.

He burst into tears. He could not believe what
had happened. He had argued with God. He had
bargained with God. God had let him—
encouraged him to do so.

It was a long time before he could get up from
his knees and start back toward the tent
compound.

9

ANOTHER CHOICE FOR LOT
Genesis 19:1-29

Lot was sitting inside the city gates when the two angels that God had sent entered the city. Inside the city gates was a wide space, almost like a market square. It was in this space that the business of the city was carried out—where the bigwigs of the city met. And Lot was one of the bigwigs.

Lot did not know that the strangers were angels, of course. To him they just seemed like extraordinary-looking men. They were tall and handsome and elegantly dressed and their faces had a strange sort of beauty. It was almost like a glow, he thought. In some peculiar way he could not put his finger on, they seemed unlike any men Lot had ever seen before.

These thoughts went through Lot's mind faster than it takes to tell it. He leapt to his feet and hurried forth to greet them.

"Greetings, travelers and strangers to our city," he said. And he bowed before them. "You must be my guests for the night." And when they hesitated, he began to insist.

And it wasn't just courtesy.

It was fear.

For a sudden realization came over Lot—of how truly wicked Sodom was. Why these strangers would not be safe there, the city was so sinful.

"You must come," he kept saying. "You *must*."

And he turned to one of his servants. "Go home at once," he said, "and give my orders to prepare a feast for these gentlemen. They will be my guests for the night."

So it was settled. Lot took the strangers home, still unaware that he was entertaining angels. He introduced them to his wife, his two daughters and

the two men his daughters were engaged to—he
already called them his sons-in-law.

The feast was spread and the evening came
and the fear in Lot's heart grew. The fear had no
name, but it was there. He knew it was there.

It was hiding in the corners.

It was lurking outside in his courtyard.

It was crouching in his closet.

Then it suddenly leapt out at him.

"God is going to destroy this city."

One of the men dropped it like a thunderbolt
into the room. Lot stared at him, his mouth gaping
open. Why these weren't men at all. These were
angels!

"He has been looking down on the sin of
Sodom, and the stench of it has come up to His
nostrils. We've come to lead you out of here in
safety, for He will surely destroy it."

"Now?" Lot said in amazement. "Leave
now?"

"It's for you to decide," the angels answered.

There was silence as Lot's family exchanged

questioning glances. Then they had a family conference.

Lot was willing to leave, for a terrible fear had come upon him. His wife wanted to leave with him—but not very much.

His daughters were willing to leave but could not imagine why they should. They were engaged and perfectly content to remain where they were.

And the sons-in-law? What? Leave? They looked at Lot as if they thought he was crazy. "After all, you were completely comfortable living here with us before," they argued. "Why should you be so high and mighty now?"

So in the end Lot and his family went to uneasy beds, shaken and undecided.

Oh well, they thought, *if this catastrophe is going to come upon us—if indeed it really is—at least we'll have a few days to think it over and decide.*

It promised to be a long, hot, sleepless night.

Lot tossed and turned on his sleeping mat and argued with himself. *There's time to decide*, he kept telling himself—*or is there*? His head was in a whirl. Perhaps this was just a warning. And what harm would it do if he stayed?

After all, he was not taking part in any of the sins of Sodom. He was just *living* there. Yes, perhaps it was just a warning—

He came to with a start. The angels were standing over him, tugging at his garments.

"Wha—"

"Hurry," they said. "It's time. You must get up."

"I must have—I must have dozed off," he said, clearing his throat. "What hour is it?"

"It will be dawn in another hour," they said. "Get up. Now. Quickly."

There was such urgency in their voices that Lot scrambled to his feet fully awake at last.

Out in the other part of the house he found his bewildered family, wandering about in a daze, picking up their various possessions, and putting them down again, still wondering whether this thing could be real, and undecided what to take with them if it was.

Lot found himself wandering about the house with them, unable to shake off the feeling that this simply wasn't real. It wasn't happening. And then—

"Now. Quickly," the angels said. "There's not a moment to lose."

He decided to beg for a little more time.

"Can you wait just a few moments?" he began.

"No. Now. You don't *have* a few moments," the angels said urgently. "Hurry. *Now*."

And he found himself grasped by the wrist with strong hands and pulled along with his wife and daughters out the door, out of the house, and up the street toward the city gate.

It was out in the morning air when the terrible truth finally hit him. There was such a stillness in the air that it was almost like a vacuum. He felt as if he couldn't breathe.

"Run!" the angels said. "Run for your lives!

Hurry!''

Lot turned to argue, but he was struck dumb with fear.

Then—

Ashes! They seemed to be coming down from the sky!

He looked about, choking, toward the angels. He heard their voices. "Don't look back. *Don't look back, any of you!*"

And he ran on, he and his wife and his daughters.

Burning embers were dropping from the sky.

The angels had disappeared.

They ran faster.

"Don't look back," Lot gasped.

Now it was raining embers and hot ash all about them.

DON'T—LOOK—BACK!!!!

"No!" he started to cry out again—but it was too late.

His wife looked back.

He stopped and stared at her in horror as she

was covered with the hot ash. She stood there, not moving, as it covered her. She remained standing—like a pillar!

He turned and ran on, his mind paralyzed now with panic, his two daughters alongside him.

There was only one word beating in his brain now.

Run. Run. Run.

The dawn came, but in the plains it was impossible to tell.

Smoke and the ashes filled the sky!

No one in Sodom or Gomorrah would have known it anyhow for there was not one person left alive. Not one animal. Not one plant.

They were all gone. Buried under ashes. And smoke poured up from the ruins.

Abraham struggled up from his couch in the tent, suddenly wide awake. He awoke with a start, surprised that he had drifted off to sleep at all. He hadn't meant to.

He struggled quickly into a cloak, hurried

outside the tent and headed quickly for the brow of the hill. There he stopped short and caught his breath.

Smoke was pouring up from all the cities of the plains. But the only city Abraham had eyes for was Sodom. Yes, Sodom was burning along with the rest of them.

And he bowed his head and wept.

He wept for the headstrong man whom he had brought up from childhood and loved as his own son.

"Oh, Lot, Lot," he sobbed, "you've thrown your life away. You've thrown your life away—"

10

THE PROMISE FULFILLED AT LAST!
Genesis 21:1-7; 20:1-16

"Eat, drink, Sire. This is a time for joy."

Abraham looked up, startled. One of his chief overseers was bending over him, his face anxious. Alongside him a servant girl was standing with a large, round basket-tray loaded with food. Abraham waved it away absently, still looking at his overseer.

"Is everything all right?" he asked. "How are things going?"

"The women tell me everything is going very well," the overseer answered.

"And Sarah?"

"Sarah is doing splendidly. There is nothing to worry about. These things take time."

Abraham sighed and stared back down at the

ground. The overseer motioned to the servant girl
to lay the tray down on the ground alongside him,
and they both went away.

Abraham was unaware that they had left. He
sat there staring, lost in his thoughts. He was
sitting a good way off from the tent. All around
him was the hustle and bustle of people moving
about, busy in the preparation of food—roasting
the calves that had been slaughtered, baking
biscuits and cakes over banked fires—jostling each
other and bumping into each other in their
excitement—and speaking in hushed whispers.
There was excitement in the air, but cautious
excitement, for underneath it all everyone was a
bit worried.

For they were awaiting the birth of a child.
Sarah's child.

Now ordinarily the birth of a child would not
cause such a stir. For men of great wealth had
many wives and countless children, so many that
it was difficult to keep track of them all. Why, a
lord and master could be informed several times

on the same day that children were born to
different wives.

But with Abraham it was different. He had
only one child by Hagar. And it was a child he
had gotten through disobedience, for he and Sarah
had run ahead of God and had not waited for God
to keep His promise.

But this child—

This child—

Abraham put his head in his hands and
groaned.

This child was to be the child God had
promised, the child that was to be born to *him and
Sarah*, the child that was to carry on his great
nation God had told him about.

And Sarah was way past the age when a child
could be born safely. Indeed, when a child could
be born at *all*.

No father, pacing the waiting room in a
maternity ward, could have been more anxious
than Abraham was.

He rocked his head from side to side and

groaned again. He was thinking about Sarah, to be sure.

He was also thinking about something else. He was thinking about a stupid blunder he had made several months before.

And it wasn't just a little blunder.

It was a *humungous* blunder.

And after God had promised him a son by Sarah.

After God had promised it!

Soon after Sodom was destroyed Abraham was traveling southward to the Negeb desert, looking for pastureland for his cattle, and he settled between Kadesh and Shur. Nothing wrong about that. One day he visited the city of Gerar. Nothing wrong about that.

But wait a minute—hold on.

The king of the city of Shur was King Abimelech. And Abimelech was forever on the lookout for beautiful women from strange lands, near and far—

Well naturally, that's what kings did in those

days. They looked for beautiful women.

And Abraham looked at Sarah. Now Sarah must have had the secret of the fountain of youth, for, incredibly, she was still beautiful. And the same old fear came up to haunt Abraham. And the same old sin came up to tempt him.

And he—and he—

And he—

Oh no—not again. Surely not again.

Oh no, he wouldn't—

He couldn't—

But he did.

He said that Sarah was his sister—and she agreed.

Not again!?!?!!!

Yup, he did. And of course, the same thing happened all over again. Abimelech took one look at Sarah and had her brought into his harem. Now Abraham might have blundered mightily, but God was still there.

For God came to King Abimelech in a dream and said, "That woman you just took into your harem is married to Abraham.''

"What?'' Abimelech said. "I am innocent. He
told me she was his sister. And she herself told
me, 'Yes, he is my brother.' I am innocent. I
haven't the slightest intention of doing anything
wrong.''

"Yes, I know,'' the Lord told Abimelech,
"and that's why I'm stopping you. So just return
her to her husband and I won't punish you. It's as
simple as that. If you don't—you're a dead man.
It's as simple as that.''

Well, the king was up at dawn. He hustled up
a meeting of all the palace personnel and he told
them what had happened. Then he sent for
Abraham and they waited in fear and trembling.

And they weren't the only ones with fear and
trembling. When the palace officials told Abraham
the king had sent for him, he knew he was in
trouble.

"What have you done to us?'' the king
bellowed. "And what have I done to you that you
should treat me like this? That you should make us

guilty of this great sin! Whatever made you think of doing such a terrible thing?"

"Well," Abraham stammered, fishing for words, "I figured you'd want my wife—and that you'd kill me to get her. And besides she is my sister. Well, at least she's my *half*-sister. And ever since we traveled from our childhood home, I've told her, 'Just say that you're my sister and then we won't get in trouble.' "

But even as he said it, he realized how foolish—how *foolish*— it sounded. And he knew how deeply he had sinned.

"Well," King Abimelech said at last, "the matter is settled. I'll give you sheep and servants—menservants and maidservants—and I will return your wife to you. And you may live around here—anywhere you please."

And then he turned to Sarah. "I am giving your 'brother' a thousand pieces of silver for damages," and he said it with sarcasm, "to compensate for any embarrassment I have caused you, to settle any claim you might have against

me." What a generous thing for Abimelech to do!
And after what Abraham did to him!

To be treated with such nobility by a *heathen
king*! Abraham squirmed in embarrassment.

"Oh," Abimelech went on, "another thing.
Your God told me you would pray for me. He said
you were some sort of a prophet."

Some prophet!

Abraham nearly squirmed out of his skin now.
It was almost more than he could bear. What a
fool he had been!

There was a long silence. And then, "God,"
Abraham finally stammered, "do not punish these
good people for what we—uh—*I*—have done. For
they have done nothing wrong. They have been
more honorable than I."

He prayed the prayer with trembling and with
great embarrassment. And so the matter was
settled. The case was closed.

Abraham was able to settle in the area that he
chose. And very soon after that, Sarah announced
to him, joyfully, that she was actually going to

have the baby. Not *a* baby. *The* baby. The baby God had promised.

It was these things that Abraham was brooding upon as he sat apart from the festivities and the hustling and the bustling about the main tent. How could he have done such a thing—told people Sarah was his sister. And *after* God had promised him a son.

After!

He had committed the same sin, not once, but twice.

He had—

Abraham was suddenly jolted out of his reverie.

At first it was an excited murmur from person to person and then it got louder and louder.

And then it rang in the air, "The baby is born!"

They pulled him to his feet. They propelled him toward the tent.

"The baby is here!"

How he ever got into the tent Abraham never knew. There was a breathless silence as he walked in.

Sarah lay on a couch of rugs. Clean linen had been spread about. The midwives and the women stood back proudly. And there, on a couch of his own, wrapped with clean linen, was a baby. A healthy, squiggling baby boy. Abraham took a step towards Sarah and knelt beside her and kissed her tenderly. Then he picked up the bundle of linen and walked to the entrance of the tent where everyone was waiting. Then with one great swoop he lifted the bundle above his head and cried triumphantly, "I have a son!"

A shout of triumph and joy filled the air.

"I have a son," he cried again, but his voice was not heard, for the din was so great.

"His name is Isaac," he said, grinning, to no one in particular. Whether or not anyone heard him did not matter.

He was too happy to care.

11

BANG! GOES THE FAMILY
Genesis 21:8-13

Celebration!
Oh happy day!
A weaning!
What?!!?
A *weaning*?
Yes, a weaning.

For Isaac was now three years old. Yes, Abraham and Sarah had a son as God had promised. And they named him Isaac according to His instructions. And Isaac meant laughter. And now he was three years old and it was time for the weaning.

Now "weaning," as you know (especially if you have baby brothers and sisters), means getting taken off the mother's breasts and put on solid food.

Now you'd think that if a child was still suckling when he was three years old—his parents would try to hush it up. But in those times it was the custom for the child to suckle until he was three, and sometimes even older.

And when he was weaned it was cause for a celebration. The wealthier the parents, the bigger the celebration.

This was a *biggy*!

All Abraham's friendly neighbors were invited and all the servants who could be spared from their labors were included. Abraham had never been happier in his life.

Everything was going swimmingly.

Abraham hoped that Ishmael would behave.

With the thought of Ishmael, an uneasy feeling started in Abraham's neck and went clear down to the end of his spine. And his stomach threatened to tie itself up in a square knot. Ishmael was in his teens and, with the years, his disposition had not improved.

Abraham had worried about it these past three

years, watching both Sarah and Hagar. Their feelings toward each other had not improved either.

And Isaac, unknowingly, had made things worse. He had lived up to his name (laughter). He had been the perfect baby from the start, smiled and gurgled and blew bubbles on cue and could goo at the drop of a head scarf. He had the patty-cake routine perfected to a fare-thee-well. And he delighted Abraham and Sarah and the servants all about him with his performances.

Hagar had regarded him with alarm.

Ishmael had regarded him with suspicion.

And they both hoped for the best.

Surely when he got to the "terrible twos"—the time when all babies turn into monsters for a year—he would show his true colors and start shouting No! to every command, and stamping his foot.

But no.

He had sailed through his "terrible twos" like a hero in a storybook. And now he was three and ready to celebrate his "weaning." And his record was just about perfect. He hadn't slipped up once.

Now in all fairness to Ishmael, you'll have to admit that it was hard to like a kid like this. He never misbehaved.

Abraham thought about all this as he watched them carefully at the weaning. Ishmael was frolicking about, and to Abraham's dismay he was behaving more obnoxiously than ever. He was dancing and prancing and doing everything in his power to get attention away from this "stupid three-year-old" who was being picked up and cuddled and carried about on people's shoulders and made such a fuss over.

Abraham glanced with increasing uneasiness at Hagar moving in the background, and sending Ishmael darting glances of warning—*Hold your tongue, Ishmael. Hold your tongue*.

And he cast uneasy glances at Sarah too. She was smiling and keeping her dignity, but her eyes were like steel.

And then Ishmael really blew it.

Right in the midst of the celebration when everyone was looking and when everyone could hear, he pranced up to Isaac and began to make sport of him.

He mocked him.

He wisecracked.

In short, he tried to make a fool of Isaac, and wound up making a fool of himself. (The Bible does not tell us what Ishmael actually did or said but we know that he attempted to make a shambles of the celebration).

For a moment it appeared as if Ishmael had spoiled the party, but everyone ignored it, or pretended to, and everything went on without a hitch.

Hagar, with one low hisssss, called Ishmael back to her side.

And so the whole thing apparently blew over.

But it hadn't blown over at all. It was not until the weaning was all over and everyone had gone home that things exploded.

In Abraham's and Sarah's tent.

"He ruined everything."

"Sarah, he ruined nothing. Everyone ignored it. The celebration went on as we had planned and everything was wonderful."

"Abraham!" Sarah faced him and her eyes were blazing. "Everything *was* not wonderful. And everything *is* not wonderful. It's not just what he did today. It's what has been going on for years. This—this—child of your *slave*—"

"He is my son, Sarah."

"He is your son!" she shrieked. "He is your son by a slave girl. It is *Isaac* who shall be your heir and shall carry on this great nation God has promised us. That slave girl and her son are not going to share your property with my son. I will not stand for it!"

"But Ishmael is still my son," Abraham began, "and it was your idea—"

But she went on as if she had not heard him. "Send them away!" she shrieked. "Send them away—both of them. You will not have a moment's peace with me until you send them away. Send them away. Do you hear?"

It was a long time before he could calm her down. Long after the people had gone home and they were on their couches, she kept saying it from her couch to his in low, steely tones. "Send them away, Abraham," she kept repeating, "or you will not have a moment's peace with me as long as you live. Send them away."

And in her own tent, Hagar tossed and turned and spoke to Ishmael in the dark, "Oh, Ishmael, Ishmael, what have you done?"

And Ishmael flopped from side to side on his couch, impatient with the whole business. What had he done?

What had he done indeed!

What had he done that he had not been doing for all these years, ever since he could remember? Only now he had done it in public. He had merely come out with the rage that had been hidden inside him all his life. He was not wanted. He had never been wanted. He could never remember a moment when he was wanted.

Well, yes, by his mother and, yes, by his father Abraham, but not by Sarah.

Never by Sarah.

He thought about Sarah for a moment. This woman, still beautiful in her old age. This woman who looked like a princess and acted like one. He had never been able to run into her arms—or even talk to her. She had always treated him like an intruder. His very insides boiled at the very thought of her.

He hated her.

And at that moment he hated everybody.

He flopped over on his side and closed his ears to his mother's pleading.

And at last he fell asleep.

Abraham tossed on his couch. Sarah's words echoed in his ears. *He is not going to share your property with my son. I won't stand for it. Send him away.*

Whatever could he do? Ishmael was his son also, and he loved him. He loved—

He got up on his elbow.

God's voice!

"Don't be upset. I'm still in control."

Abraham sat up straight now, and listened.

"Isaac is still the son I promised you. And he is still the son through whom my promise will be fulfilled."

"But, Lord," Abraham whispered in the dark, "Ishmael is still my son too. And Hagar—"

"I know," the Lord said, "And I'll make a nation of his descendants too. And don't worry about Hagar."

"What am I to do then?" Abraham said. "What am I to do?"

The answer came as a stunning blow. "Do as Sarah says."

As Sarah says? As Sarah says? Send them both away?!?!!? Abraham thought.

"Send them both away," the Lord said.

"But, *Lord*—"

"I will take care of them. Just trust me. I will still carry out my plan."

"But, Lord—?"
"I will still carry out my plan."
"But, Lord—"
Silence.
"Uh—Lord?"
The voice was gone.
Abraham knew then what he must do.
He lay awake the rest of the night.
Sometimes you could bargain with God.
And then again, sometimes you couldn't.

12

GOD AND A SLAVE GIRL
Genesis 21:14-19

Hagar stumbled along the trail in the wilderness. It had been hours—days—she couldn't remember which—since she left the compound.

Abraham came to her the morning after his all-night battle with Sarah. And he told her that the Lord had spoken to him and had told him to send her away—and that the Lord would take care of her. He strapped a provision of food upon her shoulders, and a water flask. And he kissed her tenderly on the forehead and sent her away.

And he told her that God had told him to do it. That it was God's will.

So Hagar and Ishmael left.

"We'll travel south toward Egypt," she kept

saying to Ishmael. "We will find a caravan. Don't worry, Ishmael. We will find a caravan."

Suddenly she stopped in her tracks. Ishmael had collapsed on the trail.

"Ishmael," she said. "Ishmael."

But he did not answer.

Frantic, she pulled him off the trail and into the shade of a bush. Her own tongue was swollen with thirst. The food was all gone. But water—

Water!

There was no way she could save their lives without water.

He would die. Her son Ishmael would die.

"Water," he was crying. "Water."

She left him there and stumbled a few yards beyond.

She could not bear to hear him. "I cannot watch him die," she said aloud. Then she burst into sobs.

"Hagar. Hagar."

It seemed like a voice from the sky. Had she dreamed it?

"Hagar, what is wrong?"

"I am so afraid," she choked. "Ishmael is dying."

"But God heard his very first cry," the voice came back. "Don't run away. Go back to your son and comfort him."

Comfort him?

The only way she could comfort him was with water, and there was no water anywhere except the tears streaming from her eyes.

And then she saw it.

A well.

Before her very eyes the earth seemed to open up and there was a well, filled with living, sparkling, bubbling water!

She crawled toward it.

And dipped her water flask into it.

And filled it.

And crawled back to Ishmael.

"For I will make a great nation from his descendants. The lad will live," the voice went on as she crawled back to where Ishmael was lying.

She turned him over, his sun-scorched face looked up to the sky. He was only half conscious. She let the water trickle over his parched tongue at first. Then she raised his head in her arms. He reached for the flask and drank in great gasps.

"Not too fast, Ishmael," she crooned. "Not too fast." And she let it trickle over his tongue. It was many minutes before she let him gulp it down. Then she lay beside him exhausted and poured the remainder of the water over their faces.

It was a long time before they could both crawl back to the well and drench themselves in it.

Ishmael's curly mop of hair.

And Hagar's long, flowing hair.

And Hagar kept telling Ishmael over and over and over again, "I heard the voice of God, Ishmael. He will make a great nation from your descendants. He has promised me this."

And she cupped the cool water in her hands and kept pouring it over his head and into his mouth.

And at last they both fell asleep.

13

THE HARDEST TEST OF ALL
Genesis 22:1-19

Shock!

It did not come all at once.

It came by degrees.

The day started out like any other day.
Abraham was strolling through his fields on his
way back to the tent compound. He had conferred
with his overseers and had seen that the business
of the day was running smoothly, and he was on
his way back to take his afternoon siesta in the
heat of the day. And he was thinking of what a
happy, successful man he was, and how well
things had been going.

Everything God had promised him had come
true. And all the pieces of his life were fitting into
place. Down through the years he got news of

Hagar and Ishmael. God was taking care of them
as He had promised. Hagar had found a wife for
Ishmael from Egypt. They were happily settled
and God was prospering them.

And Sarah? Why she had been as warm and
friendly as a basket of chips since Hagar and
Ishmael left.

Of course the news about Lot was not so great.
He had fled to the hills with his daughters, and
after that Abraham lost track of him completely.
But as the years went by, the ache in Abraham's
heart grew less. He had a new family to think
about now.

For it was twelve, thirteen years later now.
Isaac was in his teens! And those years with Isaac
had been the happiest years of Abraham's life.

Though God had not given him any more
specific instructions, Abraham knew that God was
near and watching over him. He sensed His
presence every moment of every day.

He supposed that God was finished at last with
any startling and earth-shaking instructions that

would spin him around and change his life. He supposed God intended to leave him to finish out his life with no more surprises. He supposed—

"Abraham!"

Abraham stopped in his tracks.

"Yes, Lord?"

"There is something I want you to do."

"Yes, Lord. Anything." And when Abraham said it, he did not know it, but he was about to face the biggest test of his life—one that would stretch his faith to the breaking point.

"Go to the land of Moriah,"

"Yes, Lord."

"And go to one of the mountains there that I'll point out to you."

"Yes, yes, Lord."

"Take Isaac with you. Isaac whom you love so much—"

"Yes, Lord." But a little quiver of fear started down Abraham's spine.

"Take him with you. And build an altar. And sacrifice—"

What???!!!!?

"But I can't do this, Lord. It's the very thing I ran away from in the city of Ur. I couldn't have heard you right."

"You heard me right."

"But, *Lord*—"

"You heard me right."

Abraham fell on his face and stayed there a long time. If he lay there long enough perhaps God would change His mind. But there was no further word. Just a great silence. The message was final.

Abraham got up at last and stumbled toward the tent compound. It was as if the sky had fallen in. It seemed to be tumbling down all about him.

Once home he could scarcely bring himself to look at either Sarah or Isaac. How could he tell Sarah what God had asked him to do? She had gone along with all his doings all her life. But not this one. Not this one. He was sure she would not go along with this one. He wouldn't put it past her to flee away with Isaac, never to be seen again!

He ate his evening meal in silence. He waited till the last minute to tell them.

"But it's three days' journey!" Sarah protested. "If you must go that far away to offer a sacrifice, why must you take Isaac?"

"Because God told me to," he said softly.

"But I *want* to go, Mother!" Isaac cried.

"Then we'll leave at dawn," Abraham said. "We'll need wood and flint for the fire. And a hank of cord to bind the sacrifice. A donkey or two. And a couple of good men." He turned to Sarah. "Will you see the servants about packing food and water?"

She nodded, her eyes troubled.

"Better go to bed," he said to Isaac. "You'll need a good night's sleep." But he turned his eyes away to hide the pain.

The next morning was the saddest morning of Abraham's life.

The journey was long and tiresome. Isaac was bored by the second day, and anxious to get there and see this mountain in Moriah.

Abraham wished the journey would never end.

But at last the lavender hills of Moriah appeared in the distance. And then, all too soon for Abraham, they were at the foothills and ready to make the climb.

"It's only a short way up," he said to Isaac. "We go the rest of the way on foot."

The servants began to unpack the donkeys. "Make camp here," he told them, "and wait for us. The lad and I will go up alone to worship. And then we'll come right back."

Why did I say we? he wondered. But he *had* said *we*, and as he said it a great peace stole over him such as he had never known before. He took the bundle of wood from a servant and put it on Isaac's shoulder. He picked up the flint and the hank of cord and tucked them in his belt where his knife was. He nodded to Isaac, and they started up the mountain.

They did not talk as they pushed on, for though it was very small for a mountain, its slope was steep enough to require all their energy.

Halfway up, Isaac stopped. "Father," he said, "we have the wood and the flint to make the fire. But where is the lamb for the sacrifice? We didn't bring a sacrifice."

Abraham had been dreading the moment when Isaac would ask this question. But suddenly all dread was gone. He found himself saying softly, "God will see to it, my son. Let's go on."

To his surprise, Isaac asked no more questions. He turned, and they plunged upward.

When they got to the place, Abraham knew it, though he had not heard God speak. It was a level place. "Here," Abraham found himself saying. "We stop here."

Isaac threw his bundle of wood to the ground and waited.

"We'll build the altar here," Abraham said. And without a word, they began to roll huge stones to the center of the level place. Some of them were so big they both had to roll them. They made a base of the bigger ones and then heaved the others up on top, stone upon stone, until at last they had a rectangular altar built, large enough to lay a sacrifice on. Then Abraham took the hank of cords from his belt, and stood there, facing Isaac. "Isaac," he said, and his voice was trembling, "God has told me to do this." And he took Isaac's hands and held them out in front of him. "*You* are the sacrifice."

Isaac was a strapping teenager. He could have fought. He could have run in panic.

He did neither.

He just stood there looking at his father. He stood still while Abraham bound him. His hands together—and then his ankles together. When Abraham finished binding Isaac's ankles, he stood up and looked at his son. And in Isaac's eyes he saw a look of such complete trust and obedience that he nearly crumpled. This had to be done quickly. He swooped Isaac up in his arms and laid him on the wood.

He took the knife from his belt. Isaac turned his head away, the tears streamed down the side of his face.

And Abraham raised the knife high above his head, ready to plunge—

"Abraham!"

God had always spoken to him in a speaking voice. But this was not a speaking voice. It was a shout!

Abraham stopped, the knife in the air. And at that moment it seemed as if the whole world stood still. Even the birds stopped singing.

"Lay down the knife, Abraham. Don't hurt the lad!"

The knife dropped to the ground.

Abraham fell to his knees beside the altar.

Then came the voice again.

"I know now that I am first in your life, Abraham. You have not withheld Isaac, even your beloved son, from me."

Abraham drew long sobbing breaths as he reached his hands up and ran them over Isaac's shoulders, over his face, and his hair.

Isaac was alive!

Isaac was alive!

Abraham sprang up like a young warrior. The strength of youth seemed to pour into him.

He untied Isaac's ankles, then his hands. And he lifted them off the altar, and they stood there in each other's arms, too overwhelmed to speak.

And then—

There was a rustling in the brush alongside them. They turned to look. It was almost as if they expected God Himself to be standing there. Or at least an angel.

But it wasn't God *or* an angel. It was a ram— his horns caught in the brush!

It was the sacrifice!

God had prepared a sacrifice after all!

As soon as they could stop their knees from wobbling, they caught it and bound its feet, and together they heaved it up on the altar and prepared it for sacrifice. As they did this, they still did not speak to each other.

Then—the voice of God again!

"I, the Lord, have sworn by myself, because you have obeyed me, I will bless you with *incredible* blessings and all the nations of the earth will be blest because of your obedience."

And then the voice was gone. They both fell on their faces; how long they lay there, neither of them knew.

It was the first time that Isaac too had heard God's voice! And it was the first time Isaac would really understand his father.

Isaac had grown up to be a man, all in these last few moments.

Later, on the way back down the mountain, Abraham kept looking sideways at his son, trudging along beside him. This new nation God was calling out hung on one person now—this young man—

And he was still alive!

14

"HE WAS MY FRIEND"
Genesis 23:1-16; 25:7-11

It was many years later.

The tent compound was quiet. Everyone was moving about slowly and speaking in whispers. Inside the main tent, Abraham was leaning over Sarah's couch. She lay there, pale and still, and in death, she looked to him like Sarai, the beautiful princess of his youth.

She had been spunky. She had made him send Hagar away. She had been jealous. She had shown all the faults of human nature. But she had followed him from youth; she had left her comfortable home in Ur to follow him. And she had lived with him in tents all through their lives together. With all her faults she had followed him without complaint. And with all her faults, she had never defied him.

He leaned over and kissed her face. And knelt beside her couch and wept.

The very next day he went down to the town of Heth and purchased a field and a cave for 400 pieces of silver. It was the first land he had actually owned since leaving the city of Ur so many years ago.

It was a burial place for Sarah.

Beautiful Sarah—

It was many years later when Abraham died. He was 175 years old!

And guess who came to his funeral?

Ishmael!

Yes, Ishmael came home again, but only long enough to help Isaac bury their father alongside his beloved Sarah.

Then Isaac and Ishmael went their separate ways again.

And their descendants never liked each other

very much. But they all had one thing in common.

They loved Abraham!

Let's think about what happened to some of these people the Bible tells us about.

Well, Terah was willing to leave the city of Ur and go with Abram. He died in the city of Haran and never got to the land God promised Abram.

What about Nahor? He was willing to go too, but he copped out in the city of Haran, and stayed there.

And Lot?

He left Ur too, and stuck with Abraham right up to the point where the prospects of wealth and importance took over—and then, even after Abraham rescued him from Sodom, he went back to that city until it was finally destroyed. And all his hopes and dreams were destroyed with it. He fled to the hills.

He is never heard from again.

And Ishmael?

Well, God knew what he would be like.

Scrappy. God told Hagar this before he was born. He lived on the "outskirts"—he never made his peace with Abraham's family.

And Hagar?

She was dragged into this family through no fault of her own. But except for her "uppity" ways at the beginning she did obey God, every step of the way. She went back and put up with Sarah's abuse until she was driven out. The last we hear of Hagar is that she got Ishmael a wife from Egypt. We do not hear of her again. But, as much as she knew how, she was obedient! And remember, she heard the voice of God!

And Sarah?

What a problem she was! To God. And to Abraham. She heard the voice of God only once (outside her tent—remember?). And then she didn't believe it. But she followed her husband to the day she died, and did what he asked in some pretty rough spots.

And Abraham?

In spite of a few blunders (and they were

biggies)—he followed God's voice to the very end
of his life. He slid a few times—

But he always got up again.

And do you know what God says about
Abraham.

"He was my friend."[1]

Wow!

"He was my friend . . ."

Note

1. James 2:23.

DICTIONARY

Abraham. Son of Terah and father of the Hebrew and Arab people. His name means "father of many nations." Abraham was also called "Friend of God."

burnt offering. In Old Testament times the Israelites kept in close touch with God by means of their offerings and sacrifices. A sacrifice was an animal given to God. In a burnt offering or sacrifice, the whole animal was burned to show respect and love for God or to atone for sin.

Isaac. The son of Abraham and Sarah. They named him Isaac which means "laughter" because they laughed first at God's promise of a child, and then because they were so happy when God kept His promise.

nomad. A person who lives in tents and moves from place to place. They usually move when seasons change or when they need new land for feeding their animals. Abraham was a nomad for much of his life.

oasis. A place in the desert where water can be found causing plants and trees to grow.

Pharaoh. Not a name but the title given to the kings in ancient Egypt. For example, an Egyptian would say "Pharaoh Neco" but an American would say "President Neco."

Sarah. The wife of Abraham and mother of Isaac. Her name means "princess."

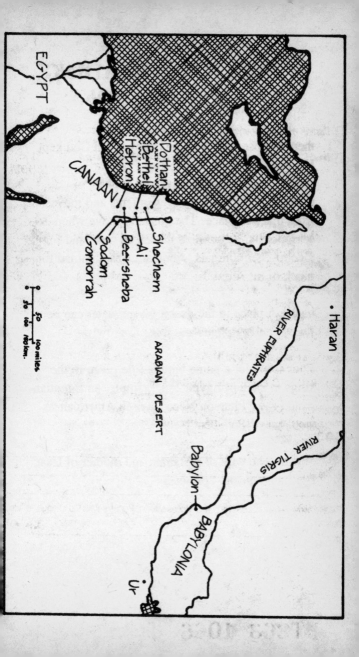

OTHER GOOD READING
from *REGAL BOOKS:*

PT263 1066